A Walk In Ola's Shoes

Written by Victoria Deodato

Illustrated By Khan

ISBN eBook: 978-1-7387338-2-8
ISBN Paperback: 978-1-7387338-1-1
ISBN Hardcover: 978-1-7387338-0-4

Dedication

Learning to walk in someone else's shoes, to see the world through their eyes, that's how peace begins. Empathy is a quality of character that can change the world.

This story was inspired by my amazing daughters and Gordy, who is a better person than I am even though he's a dog.

Dedicated to all of my loved ones, and the many wonderful students that I have had the privilege to teach over the years.

Let the adventure begin...

The sun shone so brightly; Ola loved it that way,
as she did yoga to prepare for her day.

Her morning companion was usually the cat,
but today, it was Gordy hogging most of the mat.

This floppy-eared dog was so faithful and kind,
considering the life that he'd left behind.

Gordy had been in a cage at the pound.
He was sad and alone, with no home to be found.

But when Ola walked in, it was love at first sight.
Her parents agreed; they knew it was right.

That's the thing about animals, what makes them unique
They forgive our mistakes; it's our love that they seek.

Ola loved saving Gordy after all he'd been through.
But there was so much more that she wanted to do.

As he watched her adoringly, Ola prepared
to take on injustice, how his life was spared.

A last stretch, a deep breath, then they slowly rose
to end with their favourite, the downward dog pose.

Ola did yoga to keep her mind calm.
To help more animals, she had to stay strong.

Each challenge she faced, all the battles she'd won,
and at ten and a half, she had barely begun.

Ola was cute in her own special way,
with pinchable cheeks, as her Nana would say.

She had poker-straight hair, lips like a rose,
and freckles upon freckles covered her nose.

Ola had her own style, to which she stayed true.
She loved dressing for parties, and Gordy did too.

Before she could walk, her parents would say,
"Our Ola will change the world one day."

Although she was young, she was wise beyond years.
She worked hard in school and had help from her peers.

Not only with homework or preparing for tests.
Her friends made her laugh, and that was the best.

And it was obvious right from the start
that animals held the key to her heart.

She felt a deep sadness from watching the news
when innocent creatures were hurt or abused.

Yet, she never once thought, "Well, what can I do?"
She'd come up with a plan and follow it through.

Helping animals cost money. So, she saved all she made.
When she helped 'round the house, her parents both paid

From cutting the grass and washing the car,
to walking the dog, her favourite by far.

She saved every cent and was ready to pay.
In animal rescue, it's often that way.

She started out small, but it all felt so good.
With the hurt and abandoned, she did all that she could.

Lost cats, baby birds, and sometimes a mouse.
The occasional bat would get loose in the house.

Every outing or walk or family fun day
would soon be a rescue if she had her way.

One particular day on a stroll to the store,
a Grand Opening party was outside the door.

Gordy was thrilled; there were people to greet.
If he played his cards right, he might get a treat.

There was a ribbon to cut, prizes, and cake,
and then something happened that made Ola shake.

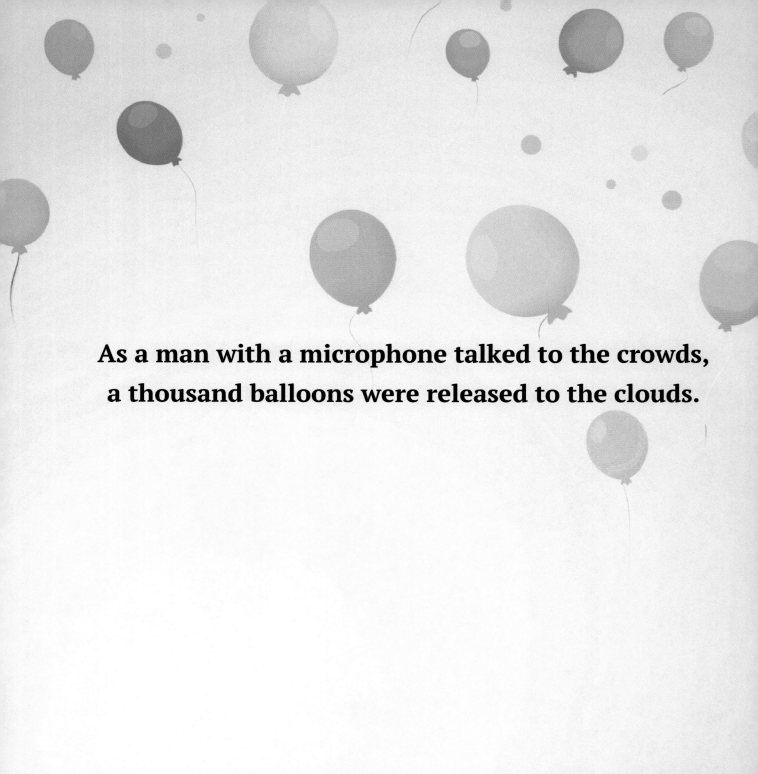

As a man with a microphone talked to the crowds,
a thousand balloons were released to the clouds.

Then Ola, the youngest attending that day,
took to the stage, and they all heard her say,

"Why would you do that? Do you know what you've done?
I'm sure that you think it was all in good fun.

I know what you feel, out of sight, out of mind,
if you followed those balloons,
do you know what you'd find?

What goes up must come down in rivers and streams.
The oceans are polluted with these harmful things.

A balloon at the surface, all deflated and slack,
makes a turtle think it's a delectable snack."

As her eyes welled with tears, she continued to speak.
She bent to pat Gordy, and he licked her cheek.

The people all listened, her mom swelled with pride.
A few of the listeners actually cried.

Then the man with the microphone finally spoke.
"I didn't know," he said, "that they make turtles choke.

Why they're beautiful creatures; I don't want them to die.
It was wrong to release those balloons to the sky."

The crowd looked at Ola; there was more to be said.
The man smiled brightly and nodded his head.

"It's not only sea turtles that suffer this fate,
they harm whales, birds, and dolphins, so we mustn't wait

Many cities pass laws, but until this is done,
spread the word to your neighbours, your friends, everyone

We all share this earth, so we must do our part,
to protect the earth's creatures, and act with our hearts."

The man smiled at Ola and shook her mom's hand.
"Thank you, Ola," he said, "for taking a stand."

And that's how it started, a one-girl crusade,
to fight for the animals, to come to their aid.

So, now that you've walked in Ola's shoes,
she needs your help to spread the news.

Ola has lots of adventures in store.
You never know; she might knock on your door.

Meet The Characters

Ola (Olivia) at 10.5

Ola & Gordy then

Olivia & Gordy now

Ola's parents th

Ola's parents now

Ola & her sister Sarah

Sarah & Ollie

Ola & Family

Nana

Gordy & BFF Ollie

Gordy's Sister Gina

Gordy's friend Shar

My Amazing Students

Noah, Cooper, Myla, Alyssa & Balian

A COUPLE OF INSPIRING TEACHERS

Andrea

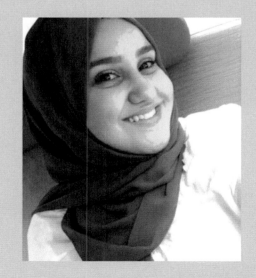

Haya

BalloonsBlow.org
Don't Let Them Go!

BalloonsBlow.org was created by two sisters that began finding so many balloons on their weekly family beach clean-ups that they knew they had to take action. Their website and social media pages are full of information about the destructive effects balloons have on the environment, and they strive to inspire and promote an eco-conscious lifestyle.

For more information or to learn how you can help, visit BalloonsBlow.org

Latex balloons are NOT eco-friendly!
Latex balloons are especially deadly to sea turtles, seabirds and marine mammals - the burst and fallen remnants mimic their prey.

4 latex balloon remnants removed from a Hawksbill sea turtle.

L. Ferris

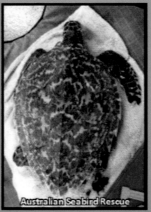

Australian Seabird Rescue

Latex balloons are not "biodegradable". They last years as deadly lures in the environment.

BalloonsBlow.org